Charlotte + Emma,

et all that you do be
done in LOVE!

♡Jessica
Parham

To Harper, Norah, and Wells:
Be you, no matter what.
Always celebrate the things
that make you different
because those things are
what make you so AWESOME!
Love, Mommy

**www.mascotbooks.com**

*Good to be Me*

©2021 Wenoha Creative, LLC. All Rights Reserved. No part of this publication may be reproduced, stored in a retrieval system or transmitted in any form by any means electronic, mechanical, or photocopying, recording or otherwise without the permission of the author.

Second printing. This Mascot Books edition in 2021.

**For more information, please contact:**
Mascot Books
620 Herndon Parkway, Suite 320
Herndon, VA 20170
info@mascotbooks.com

Library of Congress Control Number: 2020913264

CPSIA Code: PRT0121B

ISBN-13: 978-1-64543-599-0

Printed in the United States

# good to be Me

### Jessica Parham
Illustrated by Srimalie Bassani

We are **all** different,
as you can see,

But I am so happy that
I am *uniquely* me.

My hair is *different* from my friends.

What does it look like?
Well, it just depends.

Sometimes it's short,

and sometimes it's long.

I like it either way.

I cannot go wrong.

Quite often the color of my hair will change:

Pink,
Blue,
or
Purple—

I have a
wide range.

The *shape* of my
body is different, too.
Your shape is perfect
because you're uniquely
YOU!

The color of my skin is *unique* from the rest,

But no matter the color,
we should *all* feel blessed.

My mom's skin is light, and
my dad's skin is dark,
But color doesn't matter—
what matters is the heart!

Some of my friends are short, and some are tall. Everyone's height is different, and I love them all.

All of our eyes
are different, too;

Brown,
Green,
Hazel,
or Blue.

Some of my friends
love sports, and
some prefer books.

Lots of things make us different,
not just our looks!

I am happy to be me, and
I am happy you are
YOU!

Being unique is awesome, and you are, too!

Jessica Parham lives in her hometown of Richmond, Virginia with her husband, Andrew, and their three amazing kids. Her daughters and son inspire her every day to write fun kids' books. When Jessica isn't working on her newest original story, she loves baking (sourdough, anyone?), spending time with her family and friends (especially hosting at home!), and enjoying the beach (no matter the season).

 @goodtobemebook

Parents and teachers, here are some questions to help you continue the conversation on diversity and kindness.

## DIVERSITY QUESTIONS:

1. What does the word "diversity" mean to you?

2. Why is diversity important?

3. Do you think being unique or different is a positive or negative thing? Explain your thinking.

4. What can you learn from people who are different from you?

5. Do you see anyone in the book who reminds you of you? A sibling? A parent? A friend?

# KINDNESS QUESTIONS:

1. What does it mean to be kind?

2. How do you feel when people are kind? What about when they are unkind?

3. Should you be kind to people even if they look different from you?

4. What can you do to show kindness to others?

5. Can you think of a time someone was kind to you?

BONUS: What are things that you LOVE about YOURSELF? Why do you love those things?
(You are amazing, just so you know!)

I hope you are able to have meaningful conversations about diversity and kindness with your kids or students that will help them navigate the world with new understanding and compassion for others!